D0284314

DISNEY · PIXAR
FINDING
DORY

Disney · PIXAR
FINDING NEMO

4 bonus
scenes!

 phoenix international publications, inc.

Disney · PIXAR
FINDING DORY

When Dory was a little fish, she lived a happy life with her parents, Jenny and Charlie...until she got swept away by the undertow.

Before she gets lost, try finding Dory, her family, and these other undersea things:

this coral

Jenny

this sea grass

Dory

the undertow

Charlie

Dory is a forgetful fish, and she doesn't remember her parents. Now Nemo and Marlin are her family. When Dory swims along on Nemo's school trip to the stingray migration, she learns that migration is about going back to where you're from.

While Dory tries to remember where *she's* from, try to spot these familiar friends:

Pearl

Nemo

Tad

Marlin

Sheldon

Mr. Ray

The migration reminds Dory that she's from California! Marlin and Nemo travel there with Dory to help her find her parents.

Can you find these underwater creatures they meet when they arrive?

Suddenly, Dory is pulled from the water by a human...and taken inside the Marine Life Institute. There, she meets an octopus named Hank, who explains that the MLI is an aquarium. Dory realizes that this is where she was born!

As Hank and Dory sneak through the staff office to search the MLI map, try searching for these aquarium-related things:

whistle

MLI tag

MLI map

this MLI staff member

diving flippers

megaphone

these pamphlets

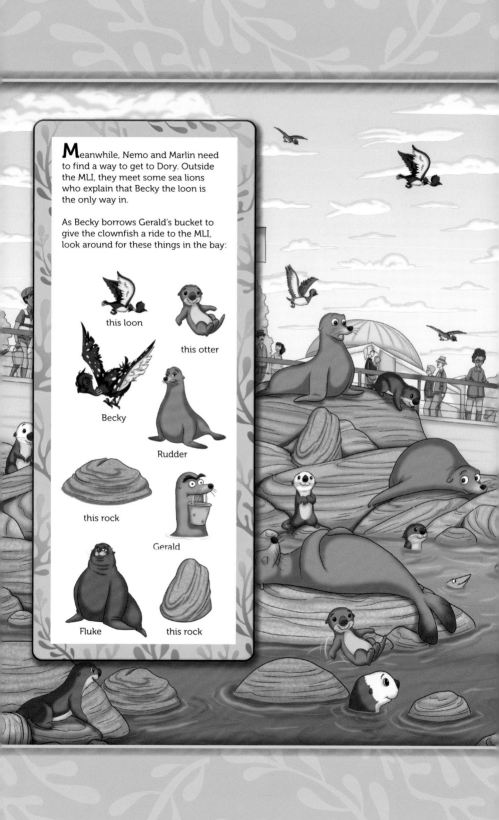

Meanwhile, Nemo and Marlin need to find a way to get to Dory. Outside the MLI, they meet some sea lions who explain that Becky the loon is the only way in.

As Becky borrows Gerald's bucket to give the clownfish a ride to the MLI, look around for these things in the bay:

this loon

this otter

Becky

Rudder

this rock

Gerald

Fluke

this rock

Dory ends up in a pool with a whale shark named Destiny and a beluga whale named Bailey. Destiny remembers Dory—they used to speak whale to each other through the pipes! Destiny tells Dory that she lived in the Open Ocean exhibit with her parents.

Before Hank takes Dory there, search the pool area for these new friends, old friends, and other things:

this sign

this
MLI staffer

Bailey

this
pool toy

Hank

this stroller

Destiny

When Dory finally finds the blue tangs (and Marlin and Nemo too), her parents aren't with them! It turns out Jenny and Charlie escaped to the ocean to wait for Dory to return.

As Dory thinks about this news, find these other blue tangs in the tank:

At last, Dory finds her parents in the ocean just outside the aquarium, and it's the happiest of happy endings! Now Dory lives on the reef with everyone she loves!

Join Dory's game of hide-and-seek and help her find her fun-loving family and friends:

Destiny

Bailey

Marlin

Jenny

Charlie

Pearl

Disney · PIXAR
FINDING NEMO

When Nemo wanders too far away from Marlin one day, he is captured by a human diver! As Marlin and Dory dive into dangerous waters to look for clues to help them find Nemo, keep an eye out for these sharks:

Chum

Bruce

Anchor

this basking shark

this whale shark

this sand shark

this tiger shark

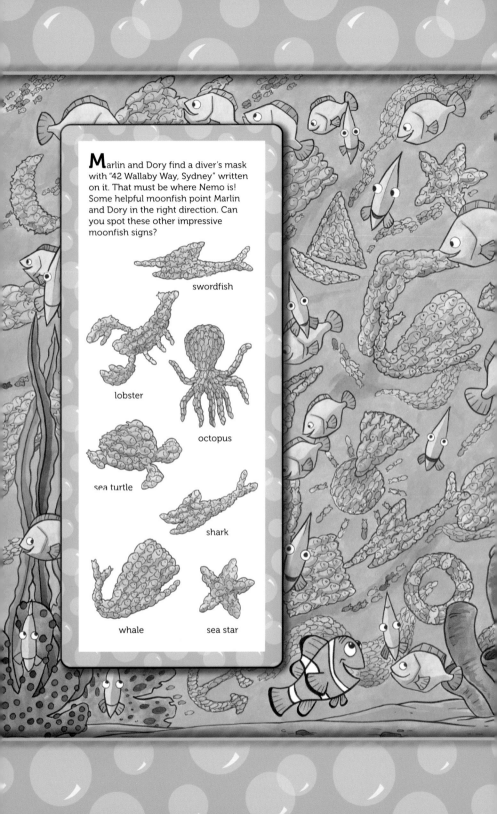

Marlin and Dory find a diver's mask with "42 Wallaby Way, Sydney" written on it. That must be where Nemo is! Some helpful moonfish point Marlin and Dory in the right direction. Can you spot these other impressive moonfish signs?

swordfish

lobster

octopus

sea turtle

shark

whale

sea star

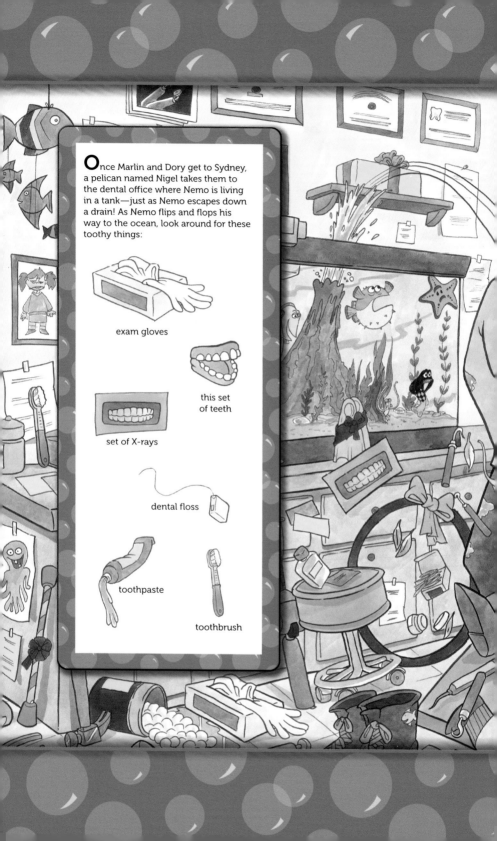

Once Marlin and Dory get to Sydney, a pelican named Nigel takes them to the dental office where Nemo is living in a tank—just as Nemo escapes down a drain! As Nemo flips and flops his way to the ocean, look around for these toothy things:

exam gloves

this set of teeth

set of X-rays

dental floss

toothpaste

toothbrush

Back in the ocean, Marlin and Nemo are reunited, but the excitement isn't over yet. The clownfish help a net full of grouper pull off an escape of their own. As the grateful groupers shower the pair with thanks, look for Marlin, Nemo, and these other fish:

Marlin

Nemo

this grouper

Dory

this grouper

this grouper

Swim back to Dory's childhood home and look for these seashells:

Migrate back to Nemo's school trip and find these stingrays on the move:

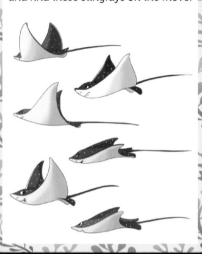

Scuttle back to the hermit crabs and look for these things that were tossed in the water:

Skip back to the MLI staff office and look for these posters:

Return to the bay outside the aquarium and find these fishy clouds:

Pop back to the pool and find these tourists:

Trek back to the blue tang tank and look for these groups of bubbles:

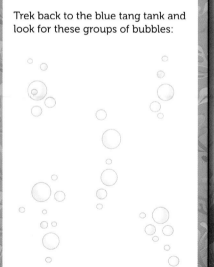

Head back to the game of hide-and-seek and help Dory find these friendly faces:

this crab

this crab

Sheldon

Nemo

Hank

Tad

Swim back to the sharks and search for these things that scuba divers have left behind:

- diver's fin
- diver's mask
- underwater flashlight
- weight belt
- scuba tank
- underwater camera

Those helpful moonfish have even more awesome impressions. Go back and find these, too:

- rocket ship
- sailboat
- diver
- arrow
- pirate flag
- life preserver

Dash back to the dental office and look for these presents the dentist bought his niece, Darla, for her birthday:

- doll
- beach ball
- baton
- diver's fins
- pair of roller skates

Go back to the groupers and find these other friends Nemo made on his adventure:

Jacques   Peach   Deb and Flo

Bloat   Gurgle   Bubbles   Gill